Foundation

F

Reading and Writing for Today's Adults

Voyager

Mary Dunn Siedow

Advisers to the Series

Mary Dunn Siedow
Director
North Carolina Literacy Resource Center
Raleigh, NC

Linda Thistlethwaite
Associate Director
The Central Illinois Adult Education Service Center
Western Illinois University
Macomb, IL

Reviewer

Linda Church
Director, Research and Development
Laubach Literacy Action

New Readers Press

Voyager: Reading and Writing for Today's Adults™ Voyager Foundation Book
ISBN 1-56420-150-3
Copyright © 1999
New Readers Press
Division of ProLiteracy Worldwide
1320 Jamesville Ave., Syracuse, New York 13210

Printed in the United States of America
9 8 7 6 5

Director of Acquisitions and Development: Christina Jagger
Content Editor: Mary Hutchison
Photography: David Revette Photography, Inc.
Developer: Learning Unlimited, Oak Park, IL
Developmental Editor: Sarah Conroy Williams
Cover Designer: Gerald Russell
Designer: Kimbrly Koennecke

ProLiteracy Worldwide and New Readers Press are not owned or sponsored by
Voyager Expanded Learning, Inc.

Contents

Alphabet

Say each letter. Write it.

A A _____   a a _____

B _____   b _____

C _____   c _____

D _____   d _____

E _____   e _____

F _____   f _____

G _____   g _____

H _____   h _____

I _____   i _____

J _____   j _____

K _____   k _____

L _____   l _____

M _____   m _____

N

O

P

Q

R

S

T

U

V

W

X

Y

Z

n

o

p

q

r

s

t

u

v

w

x

y

z

Skills Preview

A. Circle the letter that is the same.

1. **B**	(B)	D	P	E
2. **M**	N	W	V	M
3. **O**	D	C	O	D
4. **U**	V	O	V	U
5. **C**	O	C	G	O
6. **p**	d	p	b	g
7. **w**	v	m	n	w
8. **e**	c	o	e	c
9. **h**	b	h	g	d
10. **y**	j	g	y	l

B. Circle the word that is the same.

1. **bad**	pad	dab	(bad)	dad
2. **tab**	bat	tab	tad	tap
3. **can**	car	cat	can	con
4. **dip**	big	dip	drip	dig
5. **eat**	tea	ate	eat	oat
6. **bank**	back	bark	park	bank

C. Write the capital letter next to the small letter.

A B C D E F G H I J K L M N O P Q R S T U V W X Y Z

c _____   a _____   b _____   d _____   p _____

h _____   j _____   e _____   g _____   k _____

l _____   n _____   m _____   i _____   f _____

o _____   q _____   t _____   s _____   z _____

r _____   x _____   w _____   v _____   y _____

D. Copy the sentences.

1. The book is on the desk.

_____

2. Don's bank is open.

_____

3. Hal closed Don's door.

_____

4. The office is closed on Monday.

_____

Lesson 1

Bb

By the Bookstore

1. Talk, Write, and Read

A. Talk about what you see in this picture.

B. Write words with the letter **b** like **book.** You may use words from the picture.

_____   _____   _____

_____   _____   _____

C. Pick one word from your list. Make a sentence with the word.

_____

_____

D. Read your sentence out loud.

Notes for Unit 1: 1.A. Talk about the picture with students. Use words that contain the target letter frequently.
B. Follow the letter/sound lesson strategy in the Teacher's Resource Guide (TRG). **C.** Write sentences that students dictate. Have students copy them. **D.** Let students volunteer to read aloud to you or to student partners.

2. Words to Know

bank   book   subway   cab

3. Key Words

closed   is   open   Sunday   the

4. Read and Write   Read the sentences. Write the word that fits.

Open and Closed

✓book
closed
is

The ___book___ is open.

The book is _____.

The book _____ closed.

bank
is
open
The

The _____ is closed.

The bookstore is _____.

The bank _____ closed Sunday.

_____ bookstore is open Sunday.

5. In Your Own Words   Tell a story about the picture on page 8. Your teacher will write it for you.

Notes: 2. Ask students to read and talk about words that are pictured. **3.** Read each word; have students repeat.
4. Help students read each sentence and fill in the appropriate words. **5.** Conduct a Language Experience Approach (LEA) activity. See the TRG for guidance. Have students keep their copy.

Lesson 2
Dd

Don's Office

1. Talk, Write, and Read

A. Talk about what you see in this picture.

B. Write words with the letter **d** like **door.** You may use words from the picture.

_____   _____   _____

_____   _____   _____

C. Pick two words from your list. Make a sentence with each word.

1. _____

_____

2. _____

_____

D. Read your sentences out loud.

2. Words to Know

desk

door

window

shade

3. Key Words

a	an	full	has	in	office

4. Read and Write   Read the sentences. Write the word that fits.

Don's Office

full
has
desk

Don's door is closed.

Don has a _____.

The desk is _____.

The desk _____ an open book.

a
office
window

Don's _____ has a window.

The window has _____ shade.

The _____ is closed in December.

5. In Your Own Words   Tell a story about the picture on page 10. Your teacher will write it for you.

Lesson 3

Ff

Frank and His Friends

1. Talk, Write, and Read

A. Talk about what you see in this picture.

B. Write words with the letter **f** like **food.** You may use words from the picture.

_____   _____   _____

_____   _____   _____

C. Pick two words from your list. Make a sentence with each word.

1. _____

_____

2. _____

_____

D. Read your sentences out loud.

2. Words to Know

fish

friends

coffee

half

3. Key Words

and	drink	eat	Friday	his	on

4. Read and Write   Read the sentences. Write the word that fits.

Frank and His Friends

coffee
fish
friends

Frank and his friends eat fast food on Friday.

Frank and his friends eat _____

on Friday.

Frank and his _____ eat french fries.

Frank and his friends drink _____.

and
food
full

Frank eats half his fish _____

french fries.

Frank is _____.

His friends eat his _____.

5. In Your Own Words   Tell a story about the picture on page 12. Your teacher will write it for you.

Lesson 4
Hh

Hal and His Cab

1. Talk, Write, and Read

A. Talk about what you see in this picture.

B. Write words with the letter **h** like **hill.** You may use words from the picture.

_____   _____   _____

_____   _____   _____

C. Pick two words from your list. Make a sentence with each word.

1. _____

_____

2. _____

_____

D. Read your sentences out loud.

2. Words to Know

hand

hood

hose

house

3. Key Words

he	hole	new	old	puts

4. Read and Write   Read the sentences. Write the word that fits.

Hal and His Cab

hole
hood
old

Hal has an old cab.

Hal has the _____ open.

The hose is _____.

The hose has a _____.

Hal
hand
puts

Hal has a new hose in his _____.

He _____ the new hose in the cab.

_____ closes the hood.

5. In Your Own Words   Tell a story about the picture on page 14. Your teacher will write it for you.

Lesson 5

Gg
and
Jj

The Garden

1. Talk, Write, and Read

A. Talk about what you see in this picture.

B. Say words with the letter **g** like **garden,** the letter **g** like **giant,** or the letter **j** like **jacket.** Talk about the sounds that **g** and **j** make in these words.

C. Write words that have these letters.

g like **garden**	**g** like **giant**	**j** like **jacket**
_____	_____	_____
_____	_____	_____
_____	_____	_____
_____	_____	_____

Notes: 1.A. Talk about the picture as before. **B.** Explain that *g* has two common sounds (garden, giant) and that one of these (giant) is the same sound as *j*. **C.** Follow letter/sound lesson format.

2. G like Garden   In many words, **g** sounds like the **g** in **garden.** Read the words you wrote on page 16 that have this sound.

A. Choose two words from your list. Make a sentence using each word.

1. _____

2. _____

B. Read your sentences out loud.

3. Words to Know

garden   gate   wagon   dig

4. Key Words

| grow | have | May | they | up |

5. Read and Write   Read the sentences. Write the word that fits.

The Garden

| dig |
| grow |
| They |

Jan and Gus have a garden.

They _____ up the garden in May.

They _____ food in the garden.

_____ grow food for their friends.

6. **G like Giant**   In some words, **g** sounds like the **g** in **giant.** Read the words you wrote on page 16 that have this sound.

  A. Choose two words from your list. Make a sentence using each word.

  1. _____

  2. _____

  B. Read your sentences out loud.

7. **J like Jacket**   In most words, **j** sounds like the **j** in **jacket.** Read the words you wrote on page 16 that have this sound.

  A. Choose two words from your list. Make a sentence using each word.

  1. _____

  2. _____

  B. Read your sentences out loud.

8. **In Your Own Words**   Tell a story about the picture on page 16. Your teacher will write it for you.

_____

_____

_____

_____

_____

_____

9. Words to Know

garage   July   jacket   vegetables

10. Key Words

August	can	give	them	to

11. Read and Write   Read the story. Write the word that fits.

Vegetables

garden
put
wagon

Jan and Gus grow vegetables in the garden.

They _____ the vegetables in a wagon.

They put the _____ in the garage.

They close the _____ gate.

can
give
vegetables

Jan and Gus _____ eat the vegetables.

They _____ them to friends in July

and August.

They give _____ to Frank and Hal.

12. In Your Own Words   Describe what you would do if a friend gave you some vegetables. Your teacher will write it for you.

▶ Unit 1 Review Bb, Dd, Ff, Hh, Gg, and Jj

1. Words to Review Fill in the missing letter of each word. Then read the words out loud.

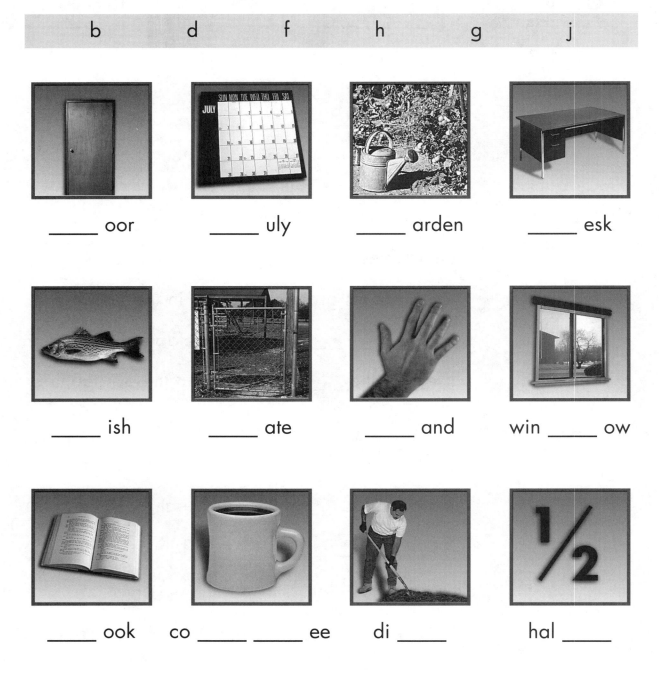

| b | d | f | h | g | j |

_____ oor _____ uly _____ arden _____ esk

_____ ish _____ ate _____ and win _____ ow

_____ ook co _____ _____ ee di _____ hal _____

Notes: 1. Have students read the six consonants. Help them write the correct consonant in the first few words. Let them complete the exercise as independently as possible.

2. Sentence Pairs Finish the sentence pairs with the word that fits. Read the sentences out loud.

coffee
December
hose
vegetables

A. Don's office has a window.

The window is closed in _____.

B. Frank and his friends eat food.

They drink _____.

C. Jan and Gus have a garden.

They grow _____ in the garden.

D. Hal has an old hose in his cab.

He puts in a new _____.

3. How Do You Know? Check the sentence that tells how you know.

A. How do you know Don is in his office?

_____ (1) His window is closed.

_____ (2) His door is open.

B. How do you know Frank eats french fries?

_____ (1) He has french fries in his hand.

_____ (2) His friends eat french fries.

C. How do you know Jan and Gus have a garden?

_____ (1) They grow vegetables.

_____ (2) They eat vegetables.

D. How do you know Hal has an old hose in his cab?

_____ (1) He puts the cab in the garage.

_____ (2) The hose has a hole.

Notes: **2.** Have students read the sentences as independently as possible and choose the word to finish each sentence. Have them read completed sentences aloud, either individually or as a group. **3.** Help students read the "How Do You Know?" questions; let them choose the more logical answer.

4. What's the Order?

A. Number the sentences in order. The first one is started for you.

1. __1__ Hal has an old hose in his cab.

_____ Hal puts in a new hose.

_____ Hal opens the hood.

2. _____ Jan and Gus dig up the vegetables.

_____ Vegetables grow in the garden.

_____ Jan and Gus give vegetables to friends.

B. Read the sentences in order out loud.

5. Writing Sentences   Make a sentence. Use all the words. Then read your sentences to someone.

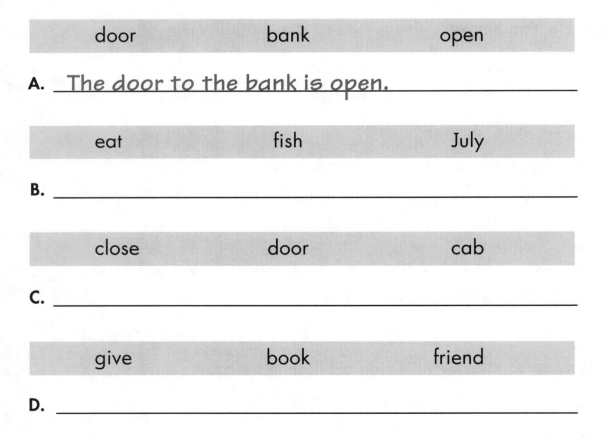

| door | bank | open |

A. _The door to the bank is open._

| eat | fish | July |

B. _____

| close | door | cab |

C. _____

| give | book | friend |

D. _____

Notes: **4.** Discuss the meaning of sequence. Help students put the first group in sequence. Have them do the second group on their own. **5.** Point out that the example is a sentence using all of the given words. Have students dictate sentences for B–D. Let them copy their sentences and read them aloud.

6. Puzzle Read the words out loud. Write words where they fit. Use all the words. Some letters are there to help you.

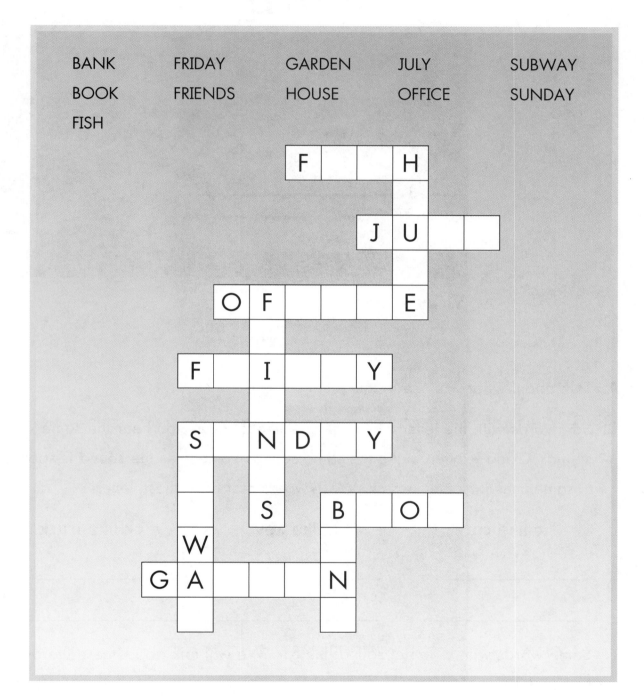

BANK   FRIDAY   GARDEN   JULY   SUBWAY

BOOK   FRIENDS   HOUSE   OFFICE   SUNDAY

FISH

Lesson 6 ▶

Cc
and
Kk

Vicky's Truck

1. Talk, Write, and Read

A. Talk about what you see in this picture.

B. Say words with the letter **c** like **car** or **k** like **key.** Do you hear the same sound? **C** and **K** often make the same sound. Sometimes the sound is spelled **c,** sometimes **k,** sometimes **ck.** Write words that have these letters.

c like **car**	k like **key**	ck like **truck**
_____	_____	_____
_____	_____	_____

Some words with **c** do not sound like **car.** We will talk about these words in Lesson 13.

C. Pick two words from your list. On another sheet of paper, make a sentence using each word. Read your sentences out loud.

Notes for Unit 2: 1.A. Talk about the picture as you did in Unit 1. **B.** Follow the letter/sound lesson strategy in the TRG. Let students read their words aloud. **C.** Write the sentences that students dictate; let them copy and read them aloud.

2. Words to Know

| car | key | truck | park |

3. Key Words

| drives | her | kids | she | work |

4. Read and Write

A. Read the story to learn about Vicky and her truck. Write the word that fits.

Vicky's Truck

her
park
truck
work

Vicky has a new truck.

She drives her truck to _____.

She drives the _____ to her house.

She can put the truck in _____ garage.

She can drive the kids to the _____.

B. What does Vicky do with her truck? Talk about it with someone.

5. In Your Own Words Would you rather drive a car or a truck? Tell about it. Your teacher will write it for you.

Notes: Do as you did in Unit 1.

Lesson 7

Ll

At the Laundromat

1. Talk, Write, and Read

A. Talk about what you see in this picture.

B. Write words with the letter **l** like **laundry.**

_____   _____   _____

_____   _____   _____

_____   _____   _____

C. Pick two words from your list. Make a sentence using each word.

1. _____

_____

2. _____

_____

D. Read your sentences out loud.

a b c d e f g h i j k **l** m n o p q r s t u v w x y z

2. Words to Know

love   laundry   clothes   children

3. Key Words

at	be	clean	Tuesday	will

4. Read and Write

A. Read to find out what Hal is doing. Write the word that fits.

At the Laundromat

clean
laundry
Tuesday
will

The Laundromat will be closed Labor Day.

On _____, the Laundromat is open.

Hal has his _____ at the Laundromat.

His clothes will be _____.

His children's clothes _____ be clean.

B. Do you do your laundry in a Laundromat? Talk about it with someone.

5. In Your Own Words
Tell about a chore you do for yourself or your family. Your teacher will write it for you.

Lesson 8
Mm

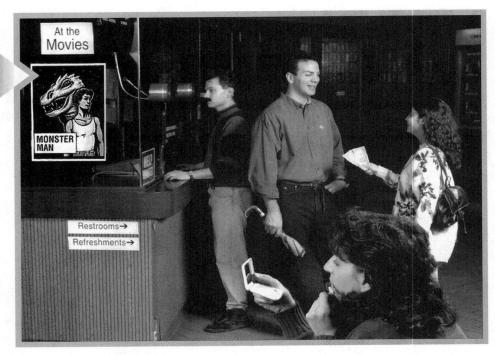

Ramon and Maria

1. Talk, Write, and Read

A. Talk about what you see in this picture.

B. Write words with the letter **m** like **man.**

_____   _____   _____

_____   _____   _____

_____   _____   _____

C. Pick two words from your list. Make a sentence using each word.

1. _____

_____

2. _____

_____

D. Read your sentences out loud.

2. Words to Know

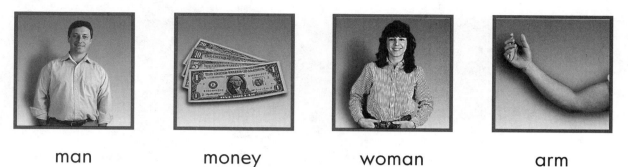

man money woman arm

3. Key Words

| for | go | into | movie | pay | some | want |

4. Read and Write

A. Read to find out what Ramon and Maria are doing. Write the word that fits.

Ramon and Maria

| money |
| movie |
| pay |
| woman |

Ramon and Maria want to go to a movie.

They get some _____ at the bank.

They _____ a man to go into the movie.

They pay a _____ for some food.

They love the _____ and the food.

B. What do Ramon and Maria do first? What do they do next? Talk about it with someone.

5. In Your Own Words
Tell about a movie you have enjoyed lately. Your teacher will write it for you.

Lesson 9

Nn

Stan's New Neighbor

1. Talk, Write, and Read

A. Talk about what you see in this picture.

B. Write words with the letter **n** like **Nancy.**

_____ _____ _____

_____ _____ _____

_____ _____ _____

C. Pick two words from your list. Make a sentence using each word.

1. _____

_____

2. _____

_____

D. Read your sentences out loud.

2. Words to Know

| neighbor | nail | dinner | newspaper |

3. Key Words

| are | gets | next | Wednesday | with |

4. Read and Write

A. Read the story to learn about Stan's new neighbor. Write the word that fits.

Stan's New Neighbor

dinner
gets
next
with

Nancy and Stan are new neighbors.

Nancy is Stan's _____ door neighbor.

Stan wants to have _____ with Nancy.

He _____ food on Wednesday.

Nancy has dinner _____ Stan.

B. What does Stan want? What does Nancy do? Talk about it with someone.

5. In Your Own Words Tell about a neighbor who is also your friend. Your teacher will write it for you.

Lesson 10
Pp

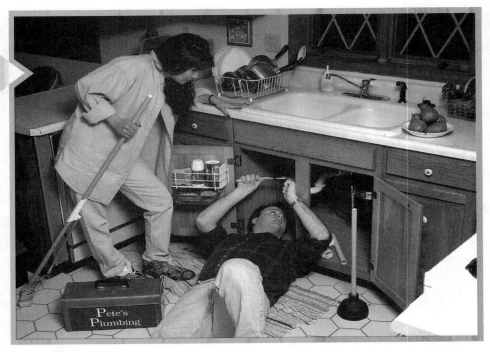

Pat's Problem

1. Talk, Write, and Read

A. Talk about what you see in this picture.

B. Write words with the letter **p** like **pipe.**

_____   _____   _____

_____   _____   _____

_____   _____   _____

C. Pick two words from your list. Make a sentence using each word.

1. _____

_____

2. _____

_____

D. Read your sentences out loud.

2. Words to Know

pipe   plumber   happy   stop

3. Key Words

calls	drips	Monday	problem	so

4. Read and Write

A. Read the story to see what Pat does about her plumbing problem. Write the word that fits.

Pat's Problem

calls
drips
happy
pipe

Pat has a problem with a pipe.

She has a pipe that _____.

On Monday, Pat _____ a plumber.

The plumber puts in a new _____.

The drip stops, so Pat is _____.

B. What would you do if you had a plumbing problem? Talk about it with someone.

5. In Your Own Words Tell about something you have had to fix at home. Your teacher will write it for you.

Lesson 11
Qq

Quinn and the Quiz Show

1. Talk, Write, and Read

A. Talk about what you see in this picture.

B. The letter **q** is almost always followed by the letter **u.** Write words with the letters **qu** like **quiz.**

_____   _____   _____

_____   _____   _____

C. Pick two words from your list. Make a sentence using each word.

1. _____

_____

2. _____

_____

D. Read your sentences out loud.

2. Words to Know

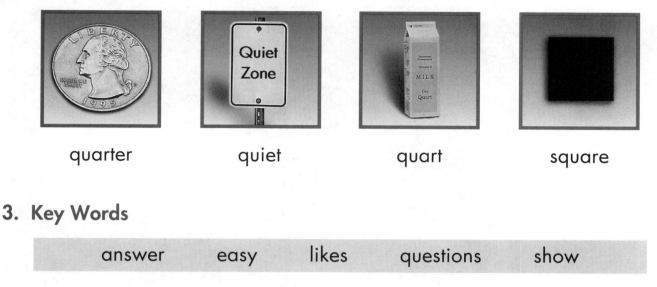

quarter   quiet   quart   square

3. Key Words

| answer | easy | likes | questions | show |

4. Read and Write

A. Read the story to learn what Quinn likes on TV. Write the word that fits.

Quinn and the Quiz Show

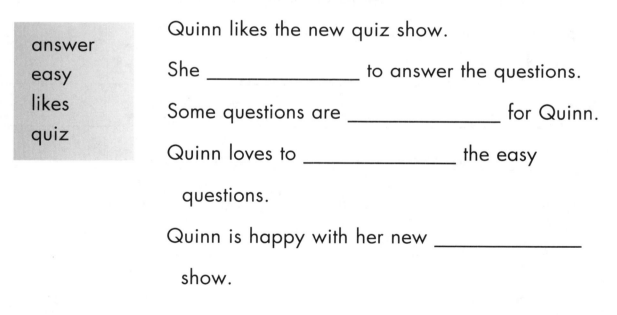

answer
easy
likes
quiz

Quinn likes the new quiz show.

She _____ to answer the questions.

Some questions are _____ for Quinn.

Quinn loves to _____ the easy

questions.

Quinn is happy with her new _____

show.

B. What does Quinn like about the quiz show? Talk about it with someone.

5. In Your Own Words
Tell about something you like to do. Your teacher will write it for you.

Lesson 12

Rr

Rainy Morning

1. Talk, Write, and Read

A. Talk about what you see in this picture.

B. Write words with the letter **r** like **rain.**

_____   _____   _____

_____   _____   _____

_____   _____   _____

C. Pick two words from your list. Make a sentence using each word.

1. _____

_____

2. _____

_____

D. Read your sentences out loud.

2. Words to Know

radio rainy morning water

3. Key Words

comes	it	March	must	their

4. Read and Write

A. Read the story to learn about Ramon and Maria's morning. Write the word that fits.

Rainy Morning

comes
must
their
water

It is a rainy morning in March.

Ramon and Maria _____ go to work.

They get up and put on _____ clothes.

Water _____ in the open window.

Ramon cleans up the _____ and they

drive to work.

B. What do Ramon and Maria do in the morning? What does he do next? Talk about it with someone.

5. In Your Own Words Tell about a time that rain spoiled your plans. Your teacher will write it for you.

▶ Unit 2 Review Cc and Kk, Ll, Mm, Nn, Pp, Qq, Rr

1. Words to Review Fill in the missing letter of each word. Then read the words out loud.

c   k   l   m   n   p   q   r

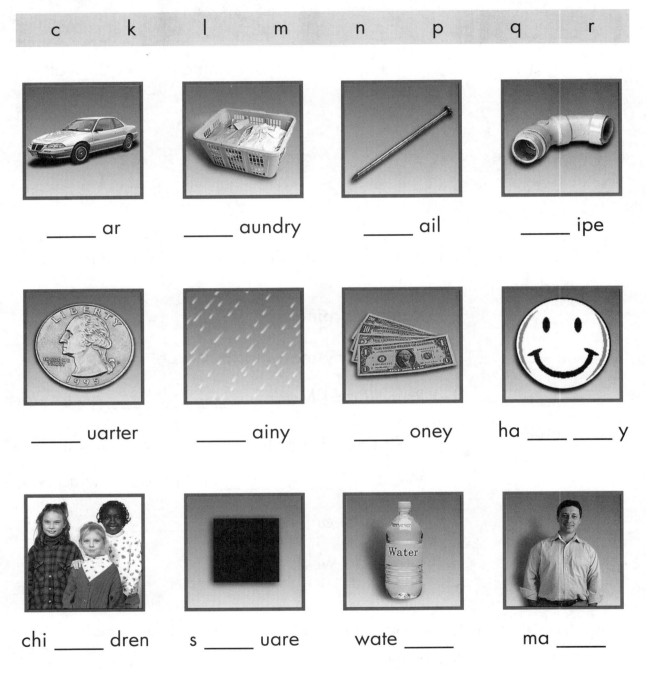

_____ ar

_____ aundry

_____ ail

_____ ipe

_____ uarter

_____ ainy

_____ oney

ha _____ _____ y

chi _____ dren

s _____ uare

wate _____

ma _____

Notes: 1. Have students read the eight consonants. Help them write the correct consonant in the first word. Let them complete the exercise as independently as possible.

2. Sentence Pairs Finish these sentence pairs with the word that fits. Read the sentences out loud.

clothes
neighbors
questions

A. Hal has some laundry.

He will clean his _____.

B. Stan is next door to Nancy.

They are friends and _____.

C. Quinn likes quiz shows.

She likes to answer easy _____.

3. What Do You Think? Check **YES** if you think these are good ideas. Check **NO** if they are not good ideas. Talk about the ideas with someone.

YES   **NO**

A. Ramon and Maria must clean the garage.
____ ____   They go to a movie.

B. Pat has a drip in a pipe.
____ ____   She calls a plumber.

C. Ramon must go to work.
____ ____   He puts on his work clothes.

D. Vicky drives her truck to work.
____ ____   She has the hood open.

Notes: **2.** Have students read the sentences as independently as possible and choose the word to finish each sentence. Have them read completed sentences aloud. **3.** Help students read the sentences.

4. What's the Order?

A. Number the sentences in order. The first one is started for you.

1. __1__ Stan wants to have dinner with Nancy.

_____ They have dinner with Hal and Quinn.

_____ Stan calls Nancy.

2. _____ Ramon and Maria drive to a movie.

_____ They love the movie.

_____ They pay money for the movie.

B. Read the sentences in order out loud.

5. Writing Sentences Make a sentence. Use all the words. Then read your sentences to someone.

must	key	truck

A. _____

children	will	love

B. _____

movie	is	quiet

C. _____

happy	to	go

D. _____

6. Puzzle Read the words out loud. Write words where they fit. Use all the words. Some letters are there to help you.

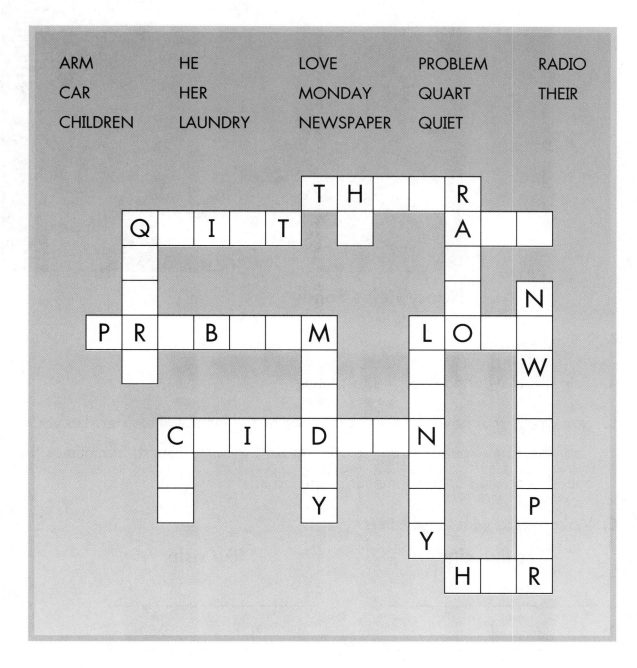

ARM   HE   LOVE   PROBLEM   RADIO

CAR   HER   MONDAY   QUART   THEIR

CHILDREN   LAUNDRY   NEWSPAPER   QUIET

Lesson 13

Cc
and
Ss

Nancy Helps Sandy

1. Talk and Write

A. Talk about what you see in this picture.

B. Say words that have the letter **c** like **city** or the letter **s** like **sister.** Do you hear the same sound? **C** and **S** often make the same sound. Sometimes the sound is spelled **c;** sometimes it is spelled **s.**

C. Write words with these letters.

c like **city**	s like **sister**
_____	_____
_____	_____
_____	_____

Remember, some words with **c** sound like **car.** We talked about these words in Lesson 6.

Notes for Unit 3: 1.A. Talk about the picture as you did in Unit 1. **B.** Explain that *c* and *s* sometimes have the same sound. **C.** Follow the letter/sound lesson strategy in the TRG.

2. Words to Know

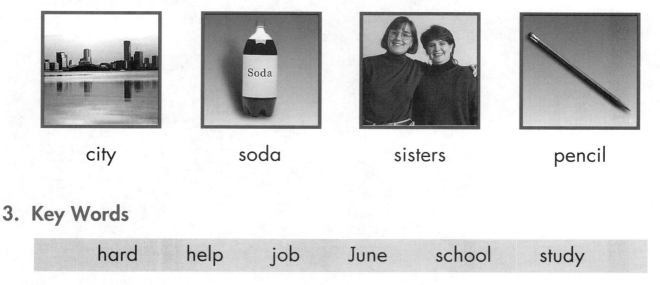

city   soda   sisters   pencil

3. Key Words

| hard | help | job | June | school | study |

4. Read and Write

A. Read the story to find why Sandy is studying. Finish the story.

Nancy Helps Sandy

Sandy is in school in the city.
She wants her GED.
She wants a new job in June.
She works hard for her GED.

Nancy and Sandy are sisters.
Nancy helps her sister study.
She helps Sandy work hard problems.
With Nancy's help, Sandy _____.

B. Why is Nancy helping Sandy study? Talk about it with someone.

5. In Your Own Words
Tell about someone who helps you study. Your teacher will write it.

Notes: 2. Ask students to read and talk about pictured words. **3.** Read each word; let students repeat. **4.** Discuss the purpose for reading the story. Ask students to read the story and finish the last sentence. Discuss question B. **5.** Conduct an LEA activity as before.

Lesson 14

Tt

1. Talk, Read, and Write

A. Talk about what you see in this picture. Read the story. Talk about the story.

Tony's Trip

In September, Tony takes a trip on the train.

He has his clothes in a suitcase.

He takes the train to the city.

Tony wants to work in the city.

B. Write words with the letter **t** like **Tony.**

_____   _____   _____

_____   _____   _____

_____   _____   _____

Notes: 1.A. Talk about the picture. Read the story aloud. Do a paired reading with students. Let students read aloud. **B.** Let students read their words aloud. They may dictate sentences with the words. Take dictation and let them copy.

2. Words to Know

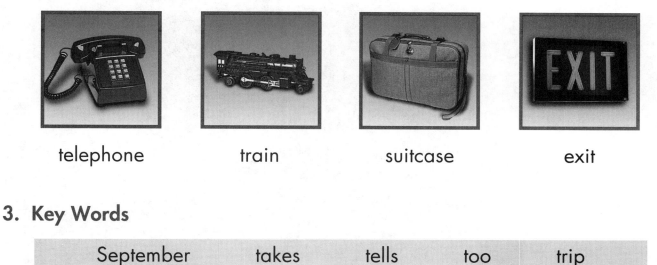

telephone   train   suitcase   exit

3. Key Words

| September | takes | tells | too | trip |

4. Read and Write

A. Read the story to find out what Tony does in the city. Finish the story.

In the City

Tony gets a new job in the city.
He likes his new job.
He loves the city, too.
Tony calls his friend Vicky on the telephone.

He tells Vicky he likes the city.
He tells her he likes his job.
He tells Vicky _____.

B. How does Tony feel about his new life in the city? Talk about it with someone.

5. In Your Own Words   Tell about a trip you would like to take. Your teacher will write it.

Lesson 15

Vv

1. Talk, Read, and Write

A. Talk about what you see in this picture. Read the story. Talk about the story.

Valentine's Day

Tony is with Vicky on Valentine's Day, February 14.
He helps Vicky with dinner.
Vicky gives Tony a valentine.
Their dinner is very good.

B. Write words with the letter **v** like **valentine.**

_____   _____   _____

_____   _____   _____

_____   _____   _____

2. Words to Know

vase   valentine   television   stove

3. Key Words

| am | dear | February | good | I | very | you |

4. Read and Write

A. Are Vicky and Tony good friends? Read the valentine Vicky gave Tony. Finish the sentences.

Dear Tony,

Some friends are old,
Some friends are new.
I am happy to have
A good friend _____.

Some friends are new,
Some friends are old.
A dear friend like you
Is _____.

B. Do you think Vicky and Tony are good friends? Talk about it with someone.

5. In Your Own Words

Tell about a good friend you have. Your teacher will write it.

Lesson 16 ▶

Ww

No Swimming

1. Talk, Read, and Write

A. Talk about what you see in this picture. Read the story. Talk about the story.

A Walk in the Woods

Wayne and Yo-Yo go for a walk.

They walk in the woods in October.

Yo-Yo wants to swim in the water.

Yo-Yo gets very wet.

B. Write words with the letter **w** like **water.**

_____ _____ _____

_____ _____ _____

_____ _____ _____

2. Words to Know

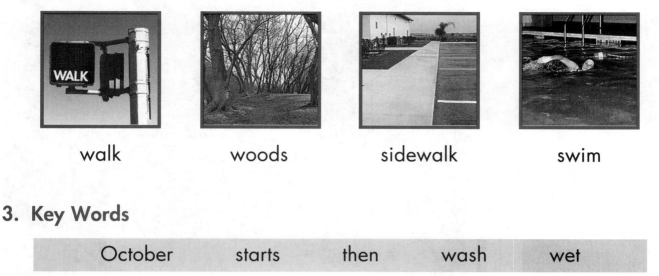

walk   woods   sidewalk   swim

3. Key Words

October   starts   then   wash   wet

4. Read and Write

A. What happens next with Wayne and Yo-Yo? Read to see what happens. Finish the story.

Wayne and Yo-Yo

Wayne wants to wash Yo-Yo.

He takes the hose.

He starts to wash Yo-Yo.

Then Yo-Yo starts to _____.

Wayne gets Yo-Yo very clean.

Then he gives Yo-Yo dinner.

For dinner, Yo-Yo gets _____.

B. What does Wayne do first? What does he do next? Talk about it with someone.

5. In Your Own Words Tell about going for a walk. Your teacher will write it.

Lesson 17

Yy

1. Talk, Read, and Write

A. Talk about what you see in this picture. Read the story. Talk about the story.

Wayne's Birthday

Wayne's birthday is November 10.

Vicky and her friends have a party for Wayne.

They eat birthday cake.

They yell "Happy Birthday" to Wayne.

B. Write words with the letter **y** like **yell.**

_____   _____   _____

_____   _____   _____

_____   _____   _____

2. Words to Know

yell   yawn   year   yield

3. Key Words

birthday   cake   November   party   this

4. Read and Write

A. What happens on Wayne's birthday? Read the story to find out. Finish the sentences.

Wayne's Party

Wayne is happy on his birthday.

He loves the party and the cake.

He gives some cake to Yo-Yo.

Yo-Yo loves _____.

Wayne wants to have a very good year.

He tells his friends,

"This party is a very good start.

I want this year to be _____."

B. How does Wayne feel about his birthday? Talk about it with someone.

5. In Your Own Words   Tell a story about your birthday. Your teacher will write it.

Lesson 18

Xx
and
Zz

1. Talk, Read, and Write

A. Talk about what you see in this picture. Read the story. Talk about the story.

Pizza for Dinner

Don and Pat want pizza for dinner.

They call the House of Pizza on the telephone.

They order a large pizza.

It comes in a large box.

They pay for the pizza.

B. **X** and **Z** are letters you will not use often. **X** often has an **e** in front of it, like in the word **exit.** Write words that have these letters.

x like **exit**   **z** like **zip**

_____   _____

_____   _____

2. Words to Know

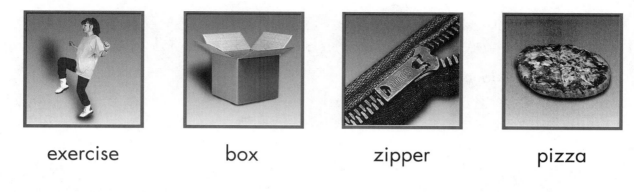

exercise   box   zipper   pizza

3. Key Words

all	feel	large	of	order

4. Read and Write

A. What do Don and Pat do after dinner? Read the story to find out.
Finish the sentences.

Exercise

Don and Pat eat all of the large pizza.

They feel very full.

They start to yawn.

They want to _____.

Then Don and Pat get up.

They start to exercise.

They exercise hard.

This helps them _____.

B. How do Don and Pat feel after dinner? What do they do next? Talk about it
with someone.

5. In Your Own Words Tell about exercises you do. Your teacher will write it.

►Unit 3 Review Cc and Ss, Tt, Vv, Ww, Yy, Xx and Zz

1. Words to Review Fill in the missing letter of each word. Then read the words out loud.

c	s	t	v	w	y	x	z

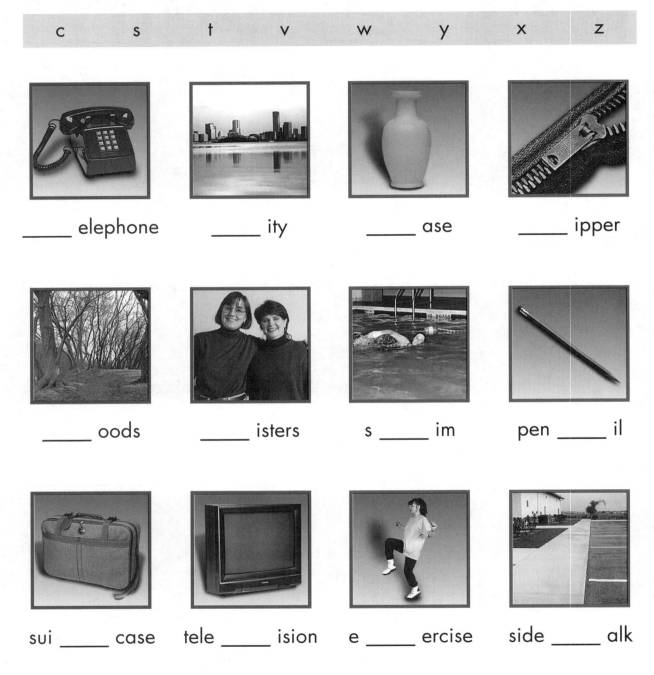

_____ elephone   _____ ity   _____ ase   _____ ipper

_____ oods   _____ isters   s _____ im   pen _____ il

sui _____ case   tele _____ ision   e _____ ercise   side _____ alk

---

Notes: **1.** Have students read the eight consonants. Let them complete the exercise as independently as possible.

2. Sentence Pairs Finish these sentence pairs with the word that fits. Read the sentences out loud.

city
exercise
study
water

A. Sandy takes the subway to school.

She can _____ on the subway.

B. Tony wants a new job.

He takes a trip to the _____.

C. Yo-Yo and Wayne go for a walk.

Yo-Yo gets wet in the _____.

D. Don and Pat eat a large pizza.

Then they _____.

3. How Do You Know? Read the stories out loud. Answer the questions. Read your answers.

A. Stan has a party for Nancy.
Nancy and her friends like the party.
They eat pizza and cake.

Was Stan's party a good one? How do you know?

_____

B. Vicky and Tony exercise in the morning.
Some mornings they walk in the woods.
Some mornings they swim in the water.

Do Vicky and Tony keep fit? How do you know?

_____

Notes: **2.** Have students read the sentences as independently as possible and choose the word to finish each sentence. Have them read completed sentences aloud, either individually or as a group. **3.** Help students read the "How Do You Know?" stories and answer the questions. Have them read their answers aloud.

4. What's the Order?

A. Number the sentences in order. The first one is started for you.

1. _1_ Don and Pat want pizza for dinner.

_____ Sandy and Nancy help them eat it.

_____ They order a large pizza.

2. _____ Yo-Yo eats the cake.

_____ Wayne has some birthday cake.

_____ Wayne gives some cake to Yo-Yo.

B. Read the sentences in order out loud.

5. Writing Sentences   Make a sentence. Use all the words. Then read your sentences to someone.

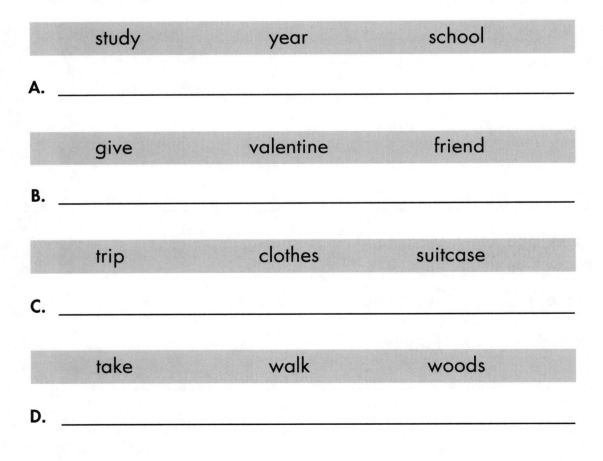

| study | year | school |

A. _____

| give | valentine | friend |

B. _____

| trip | clothes | suitcase |

C. _____

| take | walk | woods |

D. _____

Notes: **4.** Discuss the meaning of sequence. Let students complete the exercise as independently as possible.
5. Have students copy their sentences and read them aloud.

6. Puzzle Read the words out loud. Write words where they fit. Use all the words. Some letters are there to help you.

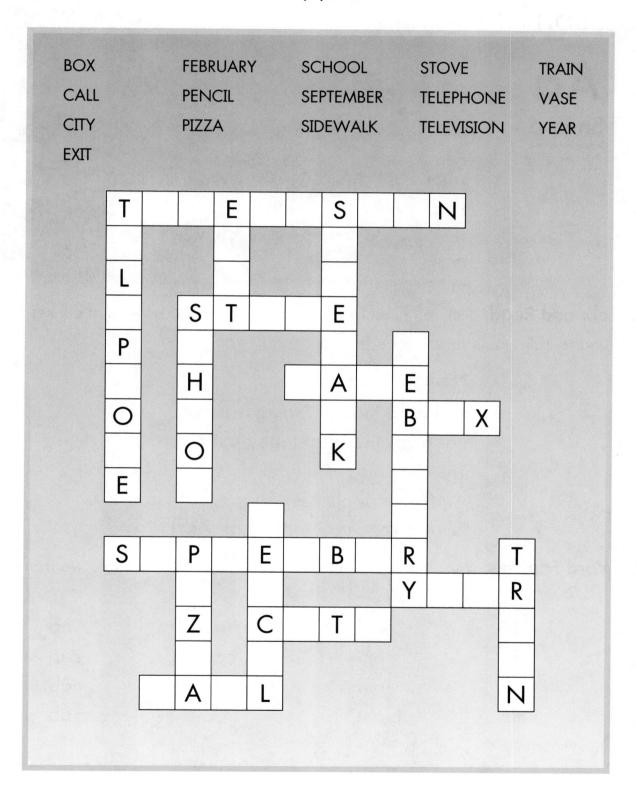

BOX   FEBRUARY   SCHOOL   STOVE   TRAIN

CALL   PENCIL   SEPTEMBER   TELEPHONE   VASE

CITY   PIZZA   SIDEWALK   TELEVISION   YEAR

EXIT

Lesson 19

Aa
Short a

1. Talk and Read Talk about what you see in this picture. Listen to the limerick. Read it. Talk about how it sounds.

Nancy's New Cat

A good friend of Nancy's is Pat.
Pat gives her a fat tabby cat.
The cat eats some ham,
And crab apple jam,
Then it naps on Nancy's new hat.

2. Word Families Read the words in these families. Write one more word in each family. You can use any words you know.

-at	-am	-ap	-ab
hat	ham	cap	cab
sat	ram	nap	nab
flat	cram	trap	crab
_____	_____	_____	_____

Notes for Unit 4: 1. Talk about the picture. Talk about rhyme and about limericks (see TRG); read the limerick.
2. Explain word families (see TRG). Have students read the words aloud and add another word to each family.

3. Words to Know

apple	back	makes	not	quite

4. Read and Write   Read the sentences. Write the word that fits.

Nancy's Hat

cab
flat
happy
nap
Pat

Nancy has a new hat.

The cat takes a _____ on Nancy's

  new hat.

This makes the hat quite _____.

Nancy is not _____.

She calls Hal in his _____.

Hal drives the cat back to _____.

5. Writing Sentences   Write sentences. Use both words. Then read your sentences out loud to someone.

sat	cab

A. _____

cat	nap

B. _____

6. In Your Own Words   Tell about a pet you know. Your teacher will write it.

Notes: 3. Read the words aloud; have students repeat. **4.** Have students read the sentences, filling in blanks with the appropriate word. **5.** Have students dictate and copy, or write sentences on their own. Have them read their sentences aloud. **6.** Conduct an LEA activity.

Lesson 20

Ee
Short e

1. **Talk and Read** Talk about what you see in this picture. Listen to the limerick. Read it. Talk about how it sounds.

   Sandy Learns to Spell
   Sandy is learning to spell.
   She writes **sell** when she wants to write **cell.**
   Oh, it is quite a mess
   When **c** sounds like **s**
   But soon she will spell very well.

2. **Word Families** Read the words in these families. Write one more word in each family. You can use any words you know.

-ed	-ell	-ess	-et
led	tell	less	get
red	yell	mess	wet
shed	spell	dress	yet
____	____	____	____

3. Words to Know

learning	soon	sounds	when	writes

4. Read and Write   Read the sentences. Write the word that fits.

A Job with a Vet

beds
fed
gets
when

Ted is a vet.

In May, Sandy _____ a job with Ted.

She cleans the pets' messy _____.

She gets the pets _____.

She tells Ted _____ the pets are

not well.

5. Writing Sentences   Write sentences. Use both words. Then read your
sentences out loud to someone.

sell	dress

A. _____

shed	pet

B. _____

6. In Your Own Words   Tell about a job that you do. Your teacher will
write it for you.

Lesson 21

I i
Short i

1. Talk and Read Talk about what you see in this picture. Listen to the limerick. Read it. Talk about how it sounds.

Vicky Cooks Fish
Vicky cooks fish on the grill.
And all of her friends eat their fill.
Vicky's friends all just sit.
They do not help a bit,
Until Vicky writes them a bill.

2. Word Families Read the words in these families. Write one more word in each family. You can use any words you know.

-ick	-ill	-ip	-it
kick	fill	dip	bit
pick	hill	zip	sit
quick	grill	chip	quit
_____	_____	_____	_____

a b c d e f g h **i** j k l m n o p q r s t u v w x y z

3. Words to Know

as	cooks	do	just	until

4. Read and Write   Read the sentences. Write the word that fits.

Dinner at Vicky's

dinner
dip
grill
sit

Vicky picks up the fish.

She fills the _____ with fish.

Her friends just _____ as she cooks.

They eat chips and _____ .

They all eat fish for _____ .

5. Writing Sentences   Write sentences. Use both words. Then read your sentences out loud to someone.

ticket	trip

A. _____

flip	grill

B. _____

6. In Your Own Words   Tell about a picnic you have been to. Your teacher will write it for you.

Lesson 22

Oo
Short o

1. **Talk and Read** Talk about what you see in this picture. Listen to the limerick. Read it. Talk about how it sounds.

A Jog in the Fog

Don takes his dog for a jog
On a day with a very thick fog.
They jog down the block
And Don hits a rock.
Now Don does not jog in the fog.

2. **Word Families** Read the words in these families. Write one more word in each family. You can use any words you know.

-ob	-ock	-og	-op
cob	mock	fog	cop
job	rock	log	mop
rob	block	frog	stop
___	___	___	___

3. Words to Know

does	down	now	Saturday

4. Read and Write Read the sentences. Write the word that fits.

Don and His Dog

| block |
| dog |
| stop |
| top |

On Saturday, Don jogs with his dog.

They jog down the _____.

They jog to the _____ of the hill.

They _____ when they get to the top.

The _____ is happy when they stop.

5. Writing Sentences Write sentences. Use both words. Then read your sentences out loud to someone.

down	rock

A. _____

job	top

B. _____

6. In Your Own Words Tell how you feel about jogging. Your teacher will write it for you.

Lesson 23

Uu
Short u

1. **Talk and Read** Talk about what you see in this picture. Listen to the limerick. Read it. Talk about how it sounds.

Gus's Lunch

For lunch my friend Gus eats a sub.
On some days he will eat a club.
With a tug on the plug
Of his cold water jug
Gus washes down all his good grub.

2. **Word Families** Read the words in these families. Write one more word in each family. You can use any words you know.

-ub	-uff	-ug	-un
rub	cuff	bug	bun
tub	puff	hug	fun
grub	scuff	plug	run
___	___	___	___

3. Words to Know

cold	January	lunch	my	push

4. Read and Write Read the sentences. Write the word that fits.

Lunch in the Sun

fun
push
sun
truck

It is a cold, sunny day in January.

Gus wants to eat lunch in the _____.

He drives his _____ to the bluff.

He has _____ until the truck gets stuck.

Gus must get Vicky to _____ with

her truck.

5. Writing Sentences Write sentences. Use both words. Then read your sentences out loud to someone.

rug	stuff

A. _____

tub	run

B. _____

6. In Your Own Words Tell what you like for lunch. Your teacher will write it for you.

Unit 4 Review Short a e i o u

1. Sentence Pairs Finish the sentence pairs. Write the word that fits.
Then read the sentences out loud.

cold	down	lunch	until
cooks	learning	make	writes

A. 1. Sandy is _____ to spell.

2. She _____ to her friend Wayne.

B. 1. Vicky _____ fish on the grill.

2. Her friends eat _____ they
are full.

C. 1. Don jogs _____ the block.

2. He does not get _____ when
he jogs.

D. 1. Gus makes a sub for _____.

2. Now and then he may _____
a club.

Notes: 1. Let students read and complete the exercise as independently as possible. Have them read each sentence
pair aloud as they complete it, checking the meaning of the sentences as they do.

2. Word Families Write one word that belongs in each family.

-at	**-am**	**-ap**	**-ab**
hat	ham	cap	cab
_____	_____	_____	_____

-ed	**-ell**	**-ess**	**-et**
bed	fell	mess	let
_____	_____	_____	_____

-ick	**-ill**	**-ip**	**-it**
sick	fill	dip	pit
_____	_____	_____	_____

-ob	**-ock**	**-og**	**-op**
sob	dock	bog	cop
_____	_____	_____	_____

-ub	**-uff**	**-ug**	**-un**
tub	muff	hug	run
_____	_____	_____	_____

Notes: 2. Have students complete the word families on their own. Have them read each family aloud to check the appropriateness of the words they've written.

3. Make Words Put the letter with the word families to make words.
Read the words.

A. l ___ ab   ___ et   ___ ip   ___ og   ___ ug

B. p ___ at   ___ et   ___ it   ___ ot   ___ uff

C. t ___ ab   ___ ell   ___ ick   ___ op   ___ ug

D. s ___ at   ___ ell   ___ ick   ___ ock   ___ un

E. b ___ at   ___ et   ___ ill   ___ og   ___ ug

4. What Do You Want to Do? Check what you would like to do. Tell why.

_____ Jog down the block.   _____ Eat a sub for lunch.

_____ Eat fish from the grill.   _____ Learn to spell.

_____ Get a cat for a pet.   _____ Work for a vet.

5. Writing Sentences Write sentences. Use all the words. Read your sentences.

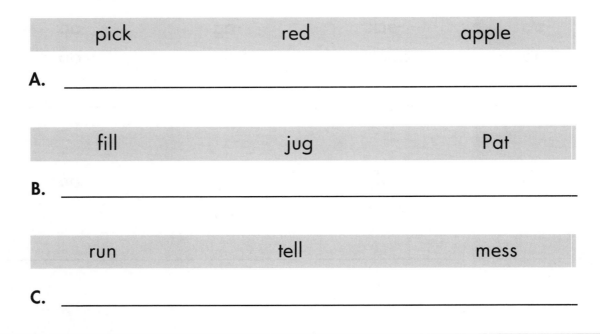

| pick | red | apple |

A. _____

| fill | jug | Pat |

B. _____

| run | tell | mess |

C. _____

Notes: 3. Have students read the words they form. **4.** Have students read the choices and check the ones they would enjoy. Have them explain their reasoning. **5.** Take dictation or let students write sentences on their own.

6. Puzzle Read the words out loud. Write words where they fit. Use all the words. Some letters are there to help you.

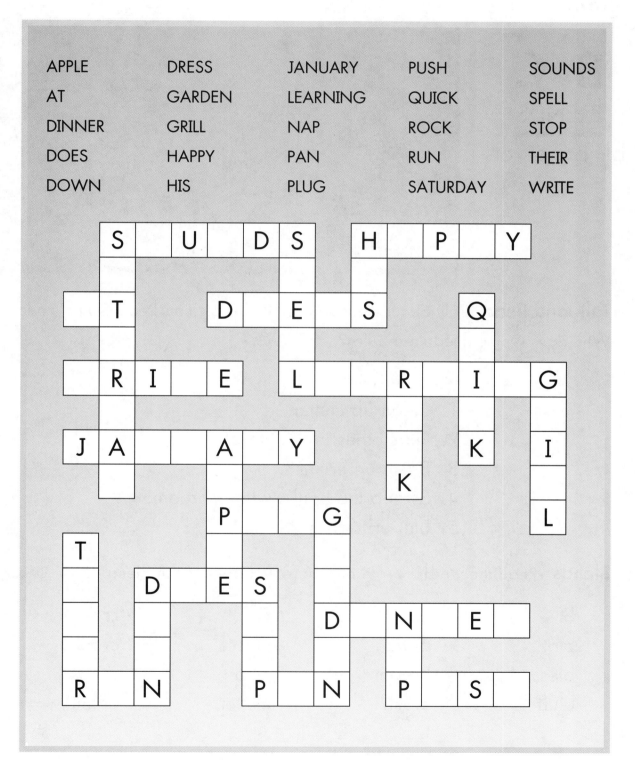

APPLE   DRESS   JANUARY   PUSH   SOUNDS

AT   GARDEN   LEARNING   QUICK   SPELL

DINNER   GRILL   NAP   ROCK   STOP

DOES   HAPPY   PAN   RUN   THEIR

DOWN   HIS   PLUG   SATURDAY   WRITE

Lesson 24

B&C
BLENDS
bl br cl cr

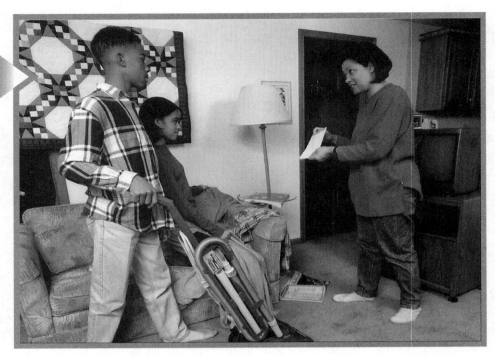

1. Talk and Read Talk about what you see in this picture. Read Quinn's rules. Why does Quinn need these rules?

Quinn's Rules

1. Clean up clutter.
2. Put clothes in the closet.
3. Brush up crumbs.
4. Sweep the house with a broom.
5. Blot up drinks you spill.

2. Blends Read the words. Write one more word with each blend.

bl	br	cl	cr
blot	bring	closet	crock
bless	broom	club	crop
bluff	brush	clutter	crumb
_____	_____	_____	_____

Notes for Unit 5: 1. Talk about the picture as before. Read the selection. Let students repeat. **2.** Read words with blends with students. Have students find words with blends from the reading. Let students add words of their own.

a **b** c d e f g h i j k l m n o p q r s t u v w x y z

3. Make Words Put the blends with the word families to make words.

bl	br	cl	cr
_____ ab	_____ am	_____ ick	_____ ock
_____ ab	_____ am	_____ ick	_____ ock

4. Words to Know

keeps	pick	rules	spill	sweep

5. Read and Think Read the story. Answer the questions after the story.

_____

Quinn keeps her house clean. The children help her. They sweep up crumbs. They pick up clutter. They put their clothes in the closet. Quinn likes a clean house.

A. Pick the better title. Write it above the story.

_____ (1) Quinn's House

_____ (2) Quinn's Job

B. What do the children do with clutter?

_____ (1) pick it up

_____ (2) sweep it up

C. What can you tell about Quinn's children?

_____ (1) They help with the housework.

_____ (2) They like to run.

6. In Your Own Words Tell about the rules you would write for people in your home. Your teacher will write it for you.

Notes: **3.** Demonstrate how to match blends and word families to make words. Have students read the words. **4.** Read the words aloud; have students repeat. **5.** Read the story; let students repeat. Read each question and let students choose the correct answer. **6.** Conduct an LEA activity.

Lesson 25

D&F
BLENDS
dr fl fr

1. Talk and Read Talk about what you see in this picture. Read this story to find out about Frank's problem.

Frank's Problem

Frank works for a flower shop. He drives the truck. Frank puts fresh flowers on the floor of the truck. When Frank drives, the flowers flip over. Flowers drop on the floor and break.

2. Blends Read the words with these blends. Write one more word with each blend.

dr	fl	fr
drag	flip	Frank
drip	floor	fresh
drop	flower	friend
_____	_____	_____

a b c d e f g h i j k l m n o p q r s t u v w x y z

3. Make Words   Put the blends with the word families to make words.

dr	fl	fr

_____ ag   _____ esh   _____ ip   _____ op

_____ ag   _____ esh   _____ ip   _____ op

4. Words to Know

break	holds	over	plan	shop

5. Read and Think   Read the story. Answer the questions after the story.

_____

Frank has a plan. He drags a large box to the truck. He nails
it to the floor. The box holds the flowers. Now the flowers do
not flip over. Now they do not drop and break.

A. Pick the better title. Write it above the story.

_____ (1) Flowers in the Truck

_____ (2) Frank's Plan

B. What was Frank's plan?

_____ (1) nail a box to the floor to hold the flowers

_____ (2) put the flowers on the floor of the truck

C. What do you think of Frank's plan? Talk about it with someone.

6. In Your Own Words   Tell about how you have solved a problem. Your
teacher will write it for you.

Lesson 26

G&P
BLENDS
gl gr pl pr

1. **Talk and Read** Talk about what you see in this picture. Read about Sandy's hopes for the future.

Graduation

In April, Sandy gets her GED diploma. Her family comes to the program. Her friends come, too. Her family and friends are happy for her. Sandy is glad they are proud. Now she plans to find a better job.

2. **Blends** Read the words with beginning blends. Write one more word with each blend.

gl	gr	pl	pr
glad	graduation	plan	press
glass	grand	plug	program
gloom	grill	plumber	proud
_____	_____	_____	_____

3. Make Words   Put the blends with the word families to make words.

gl	gr	pl	pr
_____ ass	_____ and	_____ op	_____ um
_____ ass	_____ and	_____ op	_____ um

4. Words to Know

applies	April	better	diploma	find

5. Read and Think   Read the story. Answer the questions after the story.

_____

Sandy has her GED. Now she wants a better job. She
applies for a job at Grand Press. She gets the job! She
is proud. She is glad she has her GED. She is glad
she works at Grand Press.

A. Pick the better title. Write it above the story.

_____ (1) A Better Job

_____ (2) Sandy Gets Her GED

B. What helped Sandy get her new job?

_____ (1) She has her GED.

_____ (2) She is proud.

C. What can you tell about Sandy?

_____ (1) She likes to have fun.

_____ (2) She wants to work.

6. In Your Own Words   Tell about the benefits of having a GED. Your teacher
will write it for you.

Lesson 27

S
BLENDS

sl sm sp st

1. **Talk and Read** Talk about what you see in this picture. Read the story. What do you think will happen next?

Stan's Spaghetti Sauce

On Thursday, Stan makes spaghetti sauce in a pot. He stirs the sauce. The sauce smells good as it steams. Stan puts the top on the pot. Then he takes a nap.

2. **Blends** Read the words with beginning blends. Write one more word with each blend.

sl	sm	sp	st
slap	smell	spaghetti	steam
sleep	smog	spell	stick
slope	smoke	spill	stove
_____	_____	_____	_____

3. Make Words Put the blends with the word families to make words.

sl	sm	sp	st
_____ ell	_____ ill	_____ ick	_____ op
_____ ell	_____ ill	_____ ick	_____ op

4. Words to Know

off	sauce	stir	Thursday	today	turns

5. Read and Think Read the story. Answer the questions after the story.

_____

Stan sleeps. The sauce spills over the pot. It sticks to the stove. Then it starts to smoke. Soon Stan smells the smoke.

Stan gets up and turns off the stove. He slaps at the smoke. He cleans up the spill. Stan is not happy. He will not have spaghetti today!

A. Pick the better title. Write it above the story.

_____ (1) Up in Smoke

_____ (2) Spaghetti for Dinner

B. What do you think Stan learned from this mess?

_____ (1) not to sleep when he cooks

_____ (2) not to clean house when he cooks

6. In Your Own Words Tell about a silly mistake you have made. Your teacher will write it for you.

Lesson 28

S & T
BLENDS

sk sn tr tw

1. **Talk and Read** Talk about what you see in this picture. Read the story. What do Ramon and Maria want to do?

Ramon and Maria

Ramon is twenty-five. Maria is twenty-two. They want to see snow. Ramon wants to learn to ski. Maria wants to learn to skate. In February, they take a trip to Twin Tree Hill.

2. **Blends** Read the words with beginning blends. Write one more word with each blend.

sk	sn	tr	tw
skate	snap	train	twenty
ski	snip	tree	twice
skid	snow	try	twin
_____	_____	_____	_____

3. Make Words   Put the blends with the word families to make words.

sk	sn	tr	tw

| _____ ack | _____ im | _____ in | _____ uck |
| _____ ack | _____ im | _____ in | _____ uck |

4. Words to Know

again	past	see	tries	well

5. Read and Think   Read the story. Answer the questions after the story.

_____

Ramon is learning to ski. He can ski down the easy slope. He tries the hard slope and skids past a tree. Ramon sticks to the easy slope.

Maria learns to skate. She slips and falls. She gets up and tries again. She learns to skate very well.

A. Pick the better title. Write it above the story.

_____ (1) Learning to Ski and Skate

_____ (2) The Easy Slope

B. What can you tell about Ramon and Maria?

_____ (1) They do not get cold.

_____ (2) They do not give up.

6. In Your Own Words   Tell about a skill or sport you would like to try. Your teacher will write it for you.

Unit 5 Review Blends beginning with B, C, D, F, G, P, S, T

1. Sentence Pairs Finish the sentence pairs. Write the word that fits.

better	comes	keep	sauce	
break	finds	rules	turns	

A. 1. Quinn tries to _____ her house clean.

2. She has _____ for her children.

B. 1. The flowers _____ when Frank drives.

2. Frank _____ a box to hold the flowers.

C. 1. Sandy's family _____ to her graduation.

2. They want her to get a _____ job.

D. 1. Stan wants to make spaghetti _____ today.

2. He _____ on the stove to cook the sauce.

Notes: 1. Let students read and complete the exercise as independently as possible. Have them read each sentence pair aloud as they complete it, checking the meaning of the sentences as they do.

2. Make Words Put blends with word families to make words. Read the words.

A.

dr	sp	gr	pl

_____ ab   _____ an   _____ ip   _____ um

_____ ab   _____ an   _____ ip   _____ um

B.

cl	st	sk	fr

_____ ill   _____ ip   _____ ock   _____ ump

_____ ill   _____ ip   _____ ock   _____ ump

C.

fl	tr	sm	cr

_____ ap   _____ ick   _____ ock   _____ ush

_____ ap   _____ ick   _____ ock   _____ ush

D.

br	pr	sl	sn

_____ ag   _____ op   _____ ug   _____ ush

_____ ag   _____ op   _____ ug   _____ ush

3. What Do You Want to Do? Check the activities that you want to do. Tell why.

_____ Ski down a hill.   _____ Clean up the house.

_____ Drive a truck.   _____ Take a trip.

_____ Get some fresh flowers.   _____ Cook some spaghetti.

Notes: 2. Let students work independently. Have them read each word aloud to be sure it is actually a word.
3. Have students read the list and check off what they'd like to do.

4. **How Do You Know?**   Read the stories out loud. Answer the questions. Read your answers.

   A. Sandy wants to help her friend Wayne get his GED. She tells him she will help him study. She tells him he can get a better job.

   Does Sandy plan to help Wayne? How do you know?

   _____

   B. Ramon and Maria like to go to movies. They like to give birthday parties for their friends. They love to take trips.

   Do Ramon and Maria like to have fun? How do you know?

   _____

5. **Writing Sentences**   Write sentences. Use all the words. Read your sentences.

drop	crumbs	floor

A. _____

like	skate	ski

B. _____

smell	flowers	fresh

C. _____

glad	stove	clean

D. _____

Notes: 4. Let students read the stories and questions. Let them write the answers on their own. Discuss their answers. **5.** Take dictation or let students write sentences on their own.

6. Puzzle Read the words out loud. Write words where they fit. Use all the words. Some letters are there to help you.

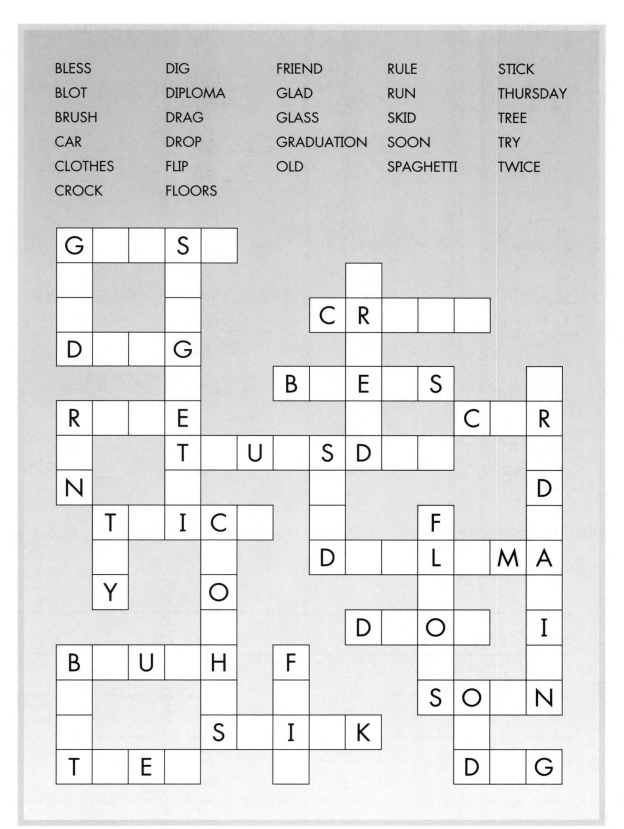

BLESS   DIG   FRIEND   RULE   STICK
BLOT   DIPLOMA   GLAD   RUN   THURSDAY
BRUSH   DRAG   GLASS   SKID   TREE
CAR   DROP   GRADUATION   SOON   TRY
CLOTHES   FLIP   OLD   SPAGHETTI   TWICE
CROCK   FLOORS

Skills Review

1. **Make Words** Put the blends with the word families to make words. Read the words.

A.	bl	dr	pr	st
	_____ ab	_____ ess	_____ op	_____ uff
	_____ ab	_____ ess	_____ op	_____ uff

B.	cl	sm	sp	tw
	_____ an	_____ ell	_____ in	_____ og
	_____ an	_____ ell	_____ in	_____ og

C.	br	fl	gr	tr
	_____ ap	_____ ab	_____ ick	_____ oom
	_____ ap	_____ ab	_____ ick	_____ oom

2. **Writing Sentences** Write sentences. Use two words from the lists above in each sentence.

A. _____

_____

B. _____

_____

Notes: Let students complete the entire Skills Review as independently as possible. For assessment guidelines, see the TRG.

3. **What's the Order?** Number the sentences in order. Then read the sentences in order out loud.

A. _____ Gus and Jan want some vegetables for dinner.
    _____ Gus cooks the vegetables in a pot on the stove.
    _____ They go to the garden and pick some vegetables.

B. _____ Hal and his children drive to the Laundromat.
    _____ They have clean clothes now.
    _____ They wash their clothes at the Laundromat.

4. **How Do You Know?** Read the stories out loud. Answer the questions. Read your answers.

A. Quinn wants to have a birthday party for Hal. She calls his friends on the telephone. She tells them when to come. She makes a birthday cake. She gets some new books to give Hal. She makes plans and works hard for the party.

Does Quinn want a good party for Hal? How do you know?

_____

B. Pat lives in a house in the city. She finds a cat in back of her house. The cat is very wet. It is quite cold, too. Pat takes him in the house. She cleans him and gives him some food. She wants to keep this cat.

How does Pat feel about the cat? How do you know?

_____

5. Read and Think Read the stories. Answer the questions. Read your answers.

A. _____

Ramon and Maria want to eat lunch in the park. They walk to the park. They take some food to eat and some cold water to drink.

At the park, Ramon and Maria walk in the woods. They eat lunch. They give some food to the fish.

1. Pick the better title. Write it above the story.

_____ (1) Fish in the Park

_____ (2) Lunch in the Park

2. What do Ramon and Maria do at the park?

_____ (1) walk in the woods and have lunch

_____ (2) eat fish and walk in the woods

B. _____

Don works with Wayne. Today, Wayne has a cold. He does not go to work.

Don must help with Wayne's work. He works hard. He does not go to lunch. He does not take a break. Don wants Wayne to come back to work soon!

1. Pick the better title. Write it above the story.

_____ (1) A Hard Day at Work

_____ (2) Don Has a Cold

2. What can you tell about Don?

_____ (1) He is a good worker.

_____ (2) He likes to take coffee breaks.

Answer Key

Unit 1

▼ Lesson 1: Bb

4. Read and Write
The **book** is open.
The book is **closed.**
The book **is** closed.
The **bank** is closed.
The bookstore is **open.**
The bank **is** closed Sunday.
The bookstore is open Sunday.

▼ Lesson 2: Dd

4. Read and Write
Don has a **desk.**
The desk is **full.**
The desk **has** an open book.
Don's **office** has a window.
The window has **a** shade.
The **window** is closed in December.

▼ Lesson 3: Ff

4. Read and Write
Frank and his friends eat **fish** on Friday.
Frank and his **friends** eat french fries.
Frank and his friends drink **coffee.**
Frank eats half his fish **and** french fries.
Frank is **full.**
His friends eat his **food.**

▼ Lesson 4: Hh

4. Read and Write
Hal has the **hood** open.
The hose is **old.**
The hose has a **hole.**
Hal has a new hose in his **hand.**
He **puts** the new hose in the cab.
Hal closes the hood.

▼ Lesson 5: Gg and Jj

5. Read and Write
They **dig** up the garden in May.
They **grow** food in the garden.
They grow food for their friends.

11. Read and Write
They **put** the vegetables in a wagon.
They put the **wagon** in the garage.
They close the **garden** gate.
Jan and Gus **can** eat the vegetables.
They **give** them to friends in July and August.
They give **vegetables** to Frank and Hal.

▼ Unit 1 Review

1. Words to Review
door, July, **g**arden, **d**esk
fish, **g**ate, **h**and, window
book, coffee, di**g**, hal**f**

2. Sentence Pairs
A. December   C. vegetables
B. coffee   D. hose

3. How Do You Know?
A. 2   B. 1   C. 1   D. 2

4. What's the Order?
A. 1. <u>1</u> Hal has an old hose in his cab.
     <u>3</u> Hal puts in a new hose.
     <u>2</u> Hal opens the hood.
  2. <u>2</u> Jan and Gus dig up the vegetables.
     <u>1</u> Vegetables grow in the garden.
     <u>3</u> Jan and Gus give vegetables to friends.

5. Writing Sentences
Sentences will vary.

6. Puzzle

Unit 2

▼ Lesson 6: Cc and Kk

4. Read and Write
A. She drives her truck to **work.**
   She drives the **truck** to her house.
   She can put the truck in **her** garage.
   She can drive the kids to the **park.**

▼ Lesson 7: Ll

4. Read and Write
A. On **Tuesday,** the Laundromat is open.
   Hal has his **laundry** at the Laundromat.
   His clothes will be **clean.**
   His children's clothes **will** be clean.

▼ Lesson 8: Mm

4. Read and Write

A. They get some **money** at the bank.
They **pay** a man to go into the movie.
They pay a **woman** for some food.
They love the **movie** and the food.

▼ Lesson 9: Nn

4. Read and Write

A. Nancy is Stan's **next** door neighbor.
Stan wants to have **dinner** with Nancy.
He **gets** food on Wednesday.
Nancy has dinner **with** Stan.

▼ Lesson 10: Pp

4. Read and Write

A. She has a pipe that **drips.**
On Monday, Pat **calls** a plumber.
The plumber puts in a new **pipe.**
The drip stops, so Pat is **happy.**

▼ Lesson 11: Qq

4. Read and Write

A. She **likes** to answer the questions.
Some questions are **easy** for Quinn.
Quinn loves to **answer** the easy questions.
Quinn is happy with her new **quiz** show.

▼ Lesson 12: Rr

4. Read and Write

A. Ramon and Maria **must** go to work.
They get up and put on **their** clothes.
Water **comes** in the open window.
Ramon cleans up the **water** and they drive
to work.

▼ Unit 2 Review

1. Words to Review

car, laundry, nail, pipe
quarter, rainy, money, happy
children, square, water, man

2. Sentence Pairs

A. clothes   B. neighbors   C. questions

3. What Do You Think?

Answers will vary.

4. What's the Order?

A. 1. <u>1</u> Stan wants to have dinner with Nancy.
 <u>3</u> They have dinner with Hal and Quinn.
 <u>2</u> Stan calls Nancy.
 2. <u>1</u> Ramon and Maria drive to a movie.
 <u>3</u> They love the movie.
 <u>2</u> They pay money for the movie.

5. Writing Sentences

Sentences will vary.

6. Puzzle

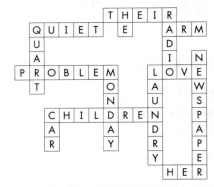

Unit 3

▼ Lessons 13–18

4. Read and Write

Sentence completions will vary.

▼ Unit 3 Review

1. Words to Review

telephone, **c**ity, **v**ase, **z**ipper
woods, **s**isters, **sw**im, pen**c**il
suitcase, tele**v**ision, e**x**ercise, side**w**alk

2. Sentence Pairs

A. study   B. city   C. water   D. exercise

3. How Do You Know?

A. We know his party is a good one because
Nancy and her friends all like the party.
B. We know Vicky and Tony keep fit because
they swim or walk in the morning.

4. What's the Order?

A. 1. <u>1</u> Don and Pat want pizza for dinner.
 <u>3</u> Sandy and Nancy help them eat it.
 <u>2</u> They order a large pizza.
 2. <u>3</u> Yo-Yo eats the cake.
 <u>1</u> Wayne has some birthday cake.
 <u>2</u> Wayne gives some cake to Yo-Yo.

5. Writing Sentences

Sentences will vary.

6. Puzzle

Unit 4

▼ Lesson 19: Aa

4. Read and Write
The cat takes a **nap** on Nancy's new hat.
This makes the hat quite **flat.**
Nancy is not **happy.**
She calls Hal in his **cab.**
Hal drives the cat back to **Pat.**

▼ Lesson 20: Ee

4. Read and Write
In May, Sandy **gets** a job with Ted.
She cleans the pets' messy **beds.**
She gets the pets **fed.**
She tells Ted **when** the pets are not well.

▼ Lesson 21: Ii

4. Read and Write
She fills the **grill** with fish.
Her friends just **sit** as she cooks.
They eat chips and **dip.**
They all eat fish for **dinner.**

▼ Lesson 22: Oo

4. Read and Write
They jog down the **block.**
They jog to the **top** of the hill.
They **stop** when they get to the top.
The **dog** is happy when they stop.

▼ Lesson 23: Uu

4. Read and Write
Gus wants to eat his lunch in the **sun.**
He drives his **truck** to the bluff.
He has **fun** until the truck gets stuck.
Gus must get Vicky to **push** with her truck.

▼ Unit 4 Review

1. Sentence Pairs
A. 1. learning   2. writes
B. 1. cooks   2. until
C. 1. down   2. cold
D. 1. lunch   2. make

2. Word Families
Additional words will vary.

3. Make Words
A. lab, let, lip, log, lug
B. pat, pet, pit, pot, puff
C. tab, tell, tick, top, tug
D. sat, sell, sick, sock, sun
E. bat, bet, bill, bog, bug

4. What Do You Want to Do?
Answers will vary.

5. Writing Sentences
Sentences will vary.

---

6. Puzzle

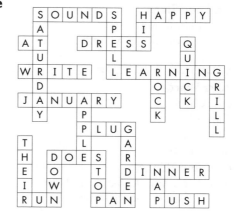

Unit 5

▼ Lesson 24: B & C Blends

3. Make Words
blab, crab
clam, cram
brick, click, crick
block, clock, crock

5. Read and Think
A. (1) Quinn's House
B. (1) pick it up
C. (1) They help with the housework.

▼ Lesson 25: D & F Blends

3. Make Words
drag, flag
flesh, fresh
drip, flip
drop, flop

5. Read and Think
A. (2) Frank's Plan
B. (1) nail a box to the floor to hold the flowers
C. Answers will vary.

▼ Lesson 26: G & P Blends

3. Make Words
glass, grass
gland, grand
glop, plop, prop
glum, plum

5. Read and Think
A. (1) A Better Job
B. (1) She has her GED.
C. (2) She wants to work.

▼ Lesson 27: S Blends

3. Make Words
smell, spell
spill, still
slick, stick
slop, stop

5. Read and Think
   A. (1) Up in Smoke
   B. (1) not to sleep when he cooks

▼ **Lesson 28: S & T Blends**

3. Make Words
   snack, track
   skim, trim
   skin, twin
   snuck, truck

5. Read and Think
   A. (1) Learning to Ski and Skate
   B. (2) They do not give up.

▼ **Unit 5 Review**

1. Sentence Pairs
   A. 1. keep   2. rules
   B. 1. break   2. finds
   C. 1. comes   2. better
   D. 1. sauce   2. turns

2. Make Words
   A. drab, grab   C. flap, trap
      span, plan   flick, trick, crick
      drip, grip   flock, smock, crock
      drum, plum   flush, crush
   B. still, skill, frill D. brag, slag, snag
      clip, skip   prop, slop
      clock, stock, frock   slug, snug
      clump, stump, frump   brush, slush

3. What Do You Want to Do?
   Answers will vary.

4. What Do You Think?
   A. Sandy plans to help Wayne. She tells him she
      will help him study.
   B. Ramon and Maria like to have fun. They like
      to go to the movies, to have parties, and to
      take trips.

5. Writing Sentences
   Sentences will vary.

6. Puzzle

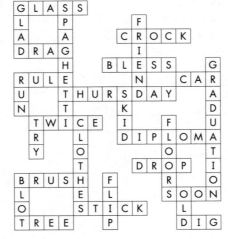

Skills Review

1. Make Words
   A. blab, drab, stab   C. flap, trap
      bless, dress, press   flab, grab
      drop, prop, stop   brick, flick, trick
      bluff, stuff   broom, groom
   B. clan, span
      smell, spell
      spin, twin
      clog, smog

2. Writing Sentences
   Sentences will vary

3. What's the Order?
   A. _1_ Gus and Jan want some vegetables
        for dinner.
      _3_ Gus cooks the vegetables in a pot on
        the stove.
      _2_ They go to the garden and pick some
        vegetables.
   B. _1_ Hal and his children drive to the
        Laundromat.
      _3_ They have clean clothes now.
      _2_ They wash their clothes at the Laundromat.

4. How do you know?
   A. Quinn wants a good party for Hal. She makes
      plans and works hard for the party.
   B. Pat likes the cat. She wants to keep him.

5. Read and Think
   A. 1. (2) Lunch in the Park
      2. (1) walk in the woods and have lunch
   B. 1. (1) A Hard Day at Work
      2. (1) He is a good worker.

Numbers

1	**one**		15	**fifteen**
2	**two**		16	**sixteen**
3	**three**		17	**seventeen**
4	**four**		18	**eighteen**
5	**five**		19	**nineteen**
6	**six**		20	**twenty**
7	**seven**		30	**thirty**
8	**eight**		40	**forty**
9	**nine**		50	**fifty**
10	**ten**		60	**sixty**
11	**eleven**		70	**seventy**
12	**twelve**		80	**eighty**
13	**thirteen**		90	**ninety**
14	**fourteen**		100	**one hundred**

Months of the Year

January	Jan.	**July**	Jul.
February	Feb.	**August**	Aug.
March	Mar.	**September**	Sept.
April	Apr.	**October**	Oct.
May	May	**November**	Nov.
June	Jun.	**December**	Dec.

Days of the Week

Sunday   Monday   Tuesday   Wednesday   Thursday   Friday   Saturday

Sunday	Sun.	**Thursday**	Thurs.
Monday	Mon.	**Friday**	Fri.
Tuesday	Tues.	**Saturday**	Sat.
Wednesday	Wed.		

Word List

Word	Lesson	Word	Lesson	Word	Lesson	Word	Lesson
a	2	clean	7	feel	18	her	6
again	28	closed	1	fill	21	hill	21
all	18	closet	24	find	26	his	3
am	15	clothes	7	fish	3	hit	22
an	2	club	23	flat	19	holds	25
and	3	clutter	24	flip	25	hole	4
answer	11	cob	22	floor	25	hood	4
apple	19	coffee	3	flower	25	hose	4
applies	26	cold	23	fog	22	house	4
April	26	comes	12	food	3	hug	23
are	9	cooks	21	for	8	I	15
arm	8	cop	22	Frank	3	in	2
as	21	crab	19	french fries	3	into	8
at	7	cram	19	fresh	25	is	1
August	5	crock	24	Friday	3	it	12
back	19	crop	24	friend	3	jacket	5
bank	1	crumb	24	frog	22	jam	19
be	7	cuff	23	full	2	Jan	5
bed	20	day	7	fun	23	January	23
better	26	dear	15	garage	5	job	13
bill	21	December	2	garden	5	jog	22
birthday	17	desk	2	gate	5	jug	23
bit	21	dig	5	GED	13	June	13
bless	24	dinner	9	get	9	July	5
block	22	dip	21	giant	5	just	21
blot	24	diploma	26	give	5	keeps	24
bluff	23	do	21	glad	26	key	6
book	1	does	22	glass	26	kick	21
bookstore	1	dog	22	gloom	26	kid	6
box	18	Don	2	go	8	labor	7
break	25	door	2	good	15	large	18
bring	24	down	22	graduation	26	Laundromat	7
broom	24	drag	25	grand	26	laundry	7
brush	24	dress	20	grill	21	learning	20
bug	23	drink	3	grow	5	led	20
bun	23	drip	10	grub	23	less	20
but	20	drive	6	Gus	5	likes	11
cab	1	drop	25	Hal	4	log	22
cake	17	easy	11	half	3	love	7
call	10	eat	3	ham	19	lunch	23
can	5	exercise	18	hand	4	makes	19
cap	19	exit	14	happy	10	man	8
car	6	family	26	hard	13	March	12
cat	19	fast	3	has	2	Maria	8
cell	20	fat	19	hat	19	May	5
children	7	February	15	have	5	mess	20
chip	21	fed	20	he	4	mock	22
city	13			help	13		

Word	Lesson	Word	Lesson	Word	Lesson	Word	Lesson
Monday	10	put	4	snip	28	tree	28
money	8	quart	11	snow	28	tries	28
mop	22	quarter	11	so	10	trip	14
morning	12	question	11	soda	13	truck	6
movie	8	quick	21	some	8	try	28
must	12	quiet	11	soon	20	tub	23
my	23	Quinn	11	sounds	20	Tuesday	7
nab	19	quit	21	spaghetti	27	tug	23
nail	9	quite	19	spell	20	turns	27
Nancy	9	quiz	11	spill	24	twenty	28
nap	19	radio	12	square	11	twice	28
neighbor	9	rainy	12	Stan	9	twin	28
new	4	ram	19	starts	16	until	21
newspaper	9	Ramon	8	steam	27	up	5
next	9	red	20	stick	27	valentine	15
not	19	rob	22	stir	27	vase	15
November	17	rock	22	stop	10	vegetables	5
now	22	rub	23	stove	15	vet	20
October	16	rules	24	stuck	23	very	15
of	18	run	23	study	13	Vicky	6
off	27	Sandy	13	sub	23	wagon	5
office	2	sat	19	subway	1	walk	16
old	4	Saturday	22	suitcase	14	want	8
on	3	sauce	27	sun	23	wash	16
open	1	school	13	Sunday	1	water	12
order	18	scuff	23	sweep	24	Wayne	16
over	25	see	28	swim	16	Wednesday	9
park	6	sell	20	tabby	19	well	20
party	17	September	14	takes	14	wet	16
past	28	shade	2	Ted	20	when	20
Pat	10	she	6	telephone	14	will	7
pay	8	shed	20	television	15	window	2
pencil	13	shop	25	tells	14	with	9
pet	20	show	11	the	1	woman	8
pick	21	sidewalk	16	their	12	woods	16
pipe	10	sisters	13	them	5	work	6
pizza	18	sit	21	then	16	writes	20
plan	25	skate	28	they	5	yawn	17
plug	23	ski	28	this	17	year	17
plumber	10	skid	28	Thursday	27	yell	17
pot	27	slap	27	to	5	yet	20
press	26	sleep	27	today	27	yield	17
problem	10	slope	27	Tony	14	you	15
program	26	smell	27	too	14	Yo-Yo	16
proud	26	smog	27	top	22	zip	21
puff	23	smoke	27	train	14	zipper	18
push	23	snap	28	trap	19		